QUEENS
OF IRELAND

IN MYTH & LEGEND

Dáithí Ó hÓgáin

INTRODUCTION

Women played leading roles in the life and lore of ancient Ireland. The many names by which the country was known - such as Éire, Banba, Fódla - were female names, and each district had its own protective goddess. These goddesses were imagined as living in hills and rivers, and their residences were said to be beautiful otherworld palaces where mortals were sometimes received as guests and treated to wondrous feasts. The goddesses, moving in and out of the real world, were material for high drama, but for interest and character their human counterparts were more than their equals. The poets and storytellers - most of them men - dwelt on the mystique which they associated with the opposite sex, but they also saw women as worthy actors on the stage of human affairs.

Dáithí Ó hÓgáin

I ngleannta séimh na héigse a bhím,
i bhfanntais péin, i ngéibh gach laoi -
an tseangbhean ghlé ba bhéasach gnaoi
do scanraigh mé, pé in Éirinn í ...

Liam Dall Ó hIfearnáin (1720-1803)

In the gentle valleys of poetry I am wont to be,
weakened as in pain, a captive of every verse-
the shining slender lady of the elegant face
startled me, whoever in Ireland she is ...

GUIDE TO PRONUNCIATION

The nearest equivalent in English spelling is indicated in each case. The sound intended by 'kh' is a fricative 'k', like the final sound in Scottish 'loch' or the 'ch' in German. The stress is normally put on the first syllable of a word :-

AILILL	" al - ill "
ADHAMAIR	" aye - mir "
BODHMHALL	" bowvel "
BRÍ LÉITH	" bree lay "
CNUCHA	" knukha "
	(i.e.Castleknock, Co.Dublin)
CONCHUBHAR	" kunkhooar ", also
	" kruhooar "
CUMHALL	" kool "
CRUNN	" krun "
DEIRDRE	" dare - derra "
ÉADAOIN	" ay - dween "
ÉADAR	" aydor "
EOCHAIDH AIREAMH	" ukhy arrov "
FEIDHLIMIDH	" fail - emmy ", also
	" file - emma "
FIONN	" f -yun ", also " finn "
	and " f - yoon "
FLIODHAIS	" fli - wish ", also
	" floosh "
LEABHARCHAM	" lavverkhom "
MACHA	" mokha "
MAOL	" mwale ", also " mweel "
	and " mool "
MEADHBH	" mayv "
MIDHIR	" mi - yirr ", also " meer "
MUIRNE	" moornay "
NAOISE	" nweesha "
TADHG	" toy - ug "
TUATHA DÉ DANANN	" tooha day donnen "

ULSTER

Navan Fort

Cooley

CONNACHT

Brí Léith

LEINSTER

Tara

Cnucha

Slieve Bloom

Hill of Allen

MUNSTER

FLIODHAIS

Fliodhais was one of the otherworld race called Tuatha Dé, who are said to have lived side by side with the Gaelic people in ancient Ireland. Her particular function was to rule over the beasts of the forest. She herded and protected the deer, and she travelled in a chariot drawn by two great stags. Her husband was Adhamair, a king of the Tuatha Dé, and during their reign cows and does were brought together every day to be milked.

It was said that she kept a fine herd of cattle, all white cows with red ears, and its leader was a great hornless cow called the Maol of Fliodhais. This cow produced the sweetest-tasting milk ever in Ireland, and so plentiful was it that one milking of the Maol would be enough to feed three hundred men, with their wives and children.

ÉADAOIN

Éadaoin was another famous woman of the Tuatha Dé. She was the wife of Midhir, who resided at Brí Léith. Midhir had another wife, who grew jealous of Éadaoin and struck her with a magic wand, turning her into a pool of water. The water became a caterpillar, and this in turn grew into a beautiful butterfly, which lovingly followed Midhir wherever he went.

However, her jealous rival caused a magic wind to rise and to blow the butterfly away from Brí Léith and out onto the sea-shore. There the transformed Éadaoin lived for seven years in misery. Eventually she managed to fly to Ulster, and she alit on the roof of a house there. The house belonged to a warrior called Éadar, and the butterfly entered it and fell into a cup from which the wife of Éadar was drinking. The woman conceived, and in this way Éadaoin was born a second time.

Eochaidh Aireamh, of the Gaelic people, became king of Ireland, but his subjects refused to pay tribute to him until he got a queen. He therefore sought out the most beautiful girl in Ireland, and found that she was Éadaoin, the daughter of Éadar. He took her to the royal fortress at Tara and married her. All went well, until one day a strange horseman arrived at Tara.

The high-king did not recognise him, but Éadaoin knew that the stranger was Midhir. Midhir began to play chess with the high-king. Eochaidh was victorious in several games, winning from Midhir horses, pigs, cattle, and sheep. Midhir also gambled with promises of performing great tasks. When he lost further games, he had to clear a large plain of stones, create a forest over another plain, and build a causeway over a great bog. Finally, Midhir won a game, and the prize that he demanded was one kiss from Éadaoin.

Eochaidh arranged that Midhir should be given his prize on a month from that day. Midhir therefore took his leave, and when his time came Eochaidh had the royal court at Tara surrounded with warriors inside and outside. However, Midhir suddenly appeared among them, took Éadaoin in his arms and carried her out through the skylight. In the form of swans they flew away together.

In a vain search for them, Eochaidh and his men dug up several otherworld cairns and raths, and when they came to Brí Léith and began to dig there, Midhir came out to them and offered to give Éadaoin back. Soon after, fifty women arrived at Tara, all looking exactly like her. Éadaoin was very skilled and very graceful at serving drink, so Eochaidh asked the fifty to do that and then chose whom he thought the best. But he chose wrong, and so Éadaoin returned to her first husband and stayed with him.

DEIRDRE

The king of Ulster, Conchubhar, was feasting one night in the house of Feidhlimidh, one of his nobles. During the feast, the wife of Feidhlimidh gave birth to a baby girl. All were pleased at this, but the king's druid prophesied that this child would be the cause of great misfortune. It was suggested that the baby should be killed, but Conchubhar would not countenance this, and instead he took her with him and had her fostered in a lonely part of his kingdom by a nurse called Leabharcham.

The girl was called Deirdre, and she grew up to be a very beautiful young woman. One day, as she watched Leabharcham's husband flaying a dead calf in the snow, a raven came and drank the blood. Deirdre remarked that the only man for her would be one with hair dark like the raven, cheeks red like the blood, and body as white as snow. Leabharcham told her that there was indeed such a young man, and his name was Naoise.

Some time later, when Naoise was hunting in the wilderness and came near to where Deirdre lived, she contrived to meet him. Naoise spoke jokingly to her. 'A fine heifer is passing by me', he said. 'Heifers are always fine', she answered wittily, 'where there are no bulls.' 'But you have the bull of the province,' said Naoise, referring to the king. 'Between the two of you, I would choose a young bull like you!' answered Deirdre.

She had won the contest of words, and she now demanded that Naoise take her away. He was reluctant, since he had heard the druid's prophecy, but Deirdre swore that he would suffer shame and derision if he refused her love. She was indeed a beautiful and striking lady, and he eventually agreed. He collected his two brothers, and the small party went to Scotland, where they would be outside of the reach of Conchubhar's vengeance.

They were a long time in Scotland, but the people of Ulster grew lonely for the company of the three gallant young men, and they prevailed on the king to allow them to return and give them a guarantee of his protection. When news of this was brought to the fugitives, Naoise and his brothers were delighted at the opportunity to return home. Deirdre was suspicious, but they persuaded her that Conchubhar would be true to his word.

They came to the royal fortress of Navan amid great rejoicing, but when they were alone in their new quarters Conchubhar sent his mercenaries to murder Naoise and his two brothers. Deirdre was disconsolate, but the king wasted no time in telling her that she must become his wife. He made her travel in the royal chariot between himself and the man who had dealt the death-blow to Naoise. She said nothing, but when Conchubhar remarked that her eye was like that of a sheep between two rams, she leaped from the chariot and dashed her head against a rock.

MACHA

A farmer of Ulster called Crunn was a widower. One day, a strange and beautiful young woman came into his house. Without saying a word, she began to clean up and look after all his household cares, and entered his bed. She brought him good fortune in all his dealings, and made him very happy. Her name was Macha, and it transpired that she had one outstanding ability above all other women - she was a great runner. Crunn noticed this, and it was among the many reasons why he was so proud of her.

The presence of this strange and marvellous woman in the house of Crunn was unknown to the rest of the Ulstermen, and Macha wished it to remain so, for she had come from the otherworld. She warned Crunn that he was never to mention her to any of his friends or associates. In time she became pregnant, and Crunn was very anxious to take good care of her. He left home on one occasion only, and that was to go to the annual assembly at the court of the king Conchubhar, at which all the men of Ulster were duty-bound to attend.

Among the many events taking place at the assembly, most attention was focussed on the chariot-racing. The pair of horses which belonged to the king proved themselves far superior to the other horses and won all the races. All the Ulstermen were loud in their praise of the horses, claiming that nothing alive could outrun them. Crunn grew impatient at this, and foolishly said that he had a woman at home who could do so easily.

When Conchubhar heard this, he ordered that the woman be brought from Crunn's house, so that they could see whether he had spoken truly. Macha protested, but was told that if she did not come her husband would be killed. She was set to race against the horses, even though her time to give birth had almost come. She won the race, but collapsed on the finishing line in the throes of death.

Before dying, Macha left a curse on the men of Ulster - that in their hour of greatest need they would be struck down with the pains which she was then suffering.

MEADHBH

The curse of Macha was fulfilled in an unexpected way. A great queen called Meadhbh ruled in Connacht, and she lorded it over her husband Ailill. One night, when Meadhbh and Ailill were engaged in pillow-talk, an argument arose over which of them had brought most wealth into their marriage. They began to compare their riches, and they found that they were equal in all things until they came to the question of cattle. They had an equal number of cows, but Ailill had a great white bull which his queen could not match.

Meadbh was angry and disappointed, for she never could suffer being overcome by anybody in a contest. She wasted no time in enquiring was there any bull in Ireland which was the equal of the white bull of Ailill, and she eventually discovered that there was indeed such an animal. It was a brown bull, and was owned by a farmer in Cooley, a district which was a protectorate of Ulster.

Meadhbh sent messengers to that farmer seeking a loan of the brown bull, and they received a favourable reply. As was the custom the messengers were treated to a fine feast in Cooley, but when they had drunk too much they began to boast that even if the bull had been refused they would have taken it by force. At this, the bull's owner changed his mind, and adamantly refused to let them have the bull.

When the messengers returned to Meadhbh, she flew into a rage and began immediately to make preparations to go and take the brown bull. Knowing that this would bring her into conflict with King Conchubhar and his Ulstermen, she assembled a massive army to attack the northern province. As she set out at the head of her mighty host, the curse of Macha fell on the men of Ulster. All of them were struck down with pains similar to a woman in childbirth, and they were unable to take the field. Meadhbh burned and ravaged their province, and took the great brown bull back to Connacht with her.

Muirne was the daughter of a druid called Tadhg who lived on the Hill of Allen in Leinster. She was carried away by the warrior Cumhall, who became her lover. Tadhg went to the high-king to complain, and as a result of this the warrior was slain in the battle of Cnucha and Muirne was left with a fatherless child. This child was the celebrated hero Fionn.

Knowing that the little Fionn was in danger from the many enemies whom his father had made, Muirne entrusted the child to the care of Cumhall's sister Bodhmhall, who lived in the lonely district around Slieve Bloom. Bodhmhall was an adept at feats of arms, and she taught all that she knew to the boy. She once saved him from a search-party of foes by hiding him in the bark of a tree, and on another occasion, when pursued by horsemen, she raced through the forests to safety with the young Fionn on her shoulders. She was pleased to see that her work was completed when one day she took him hunting on the mountains. Despite her fleetness of foot, she failed to take a wild deer, but Fionn himself captured two and brought them home to the hut.

MYTHS & LEGENDS OF IRELAND SERIES

KINGS OF IRELAND

QUEENS OF IRELAND

ANIMALS OF IRELAND

HEROES OF IRELAND

REAL IRELAND

© REAL IRELAND DESIGN LIMITED
Front Cover Design: Joe Reynolds
Text: Dáithí Ó hÓgáin MA PhD
Layout: Target Marketing Ltd.

QUEENS OF IRELAND
IN MYTH AND LEGEND
ISBN 0 946887 16 0